THE SC BANANA

— PRESENTS —

THE JUNIPER TREE

AN ULTRA-GRIM FAIRY TALE FROM THE BROTHERS GRIMM

The Scholarly Banana Presents The Juniper Tree:
An Ultra-Grim Fairy Tale from the Brothers Grimm

Copyright © 2020 Karly West

PAPERBACK ISBN 978-1-7338509-2-6   EBOOK ISBN 978-1-7338509-3-3

No bananas were harmed in the making of this book.

for the
BANANAS

SOMETHING LIKE A PREFACE

Welcome to this Scholarly deep-dive into *The Juniper Tree!* Along the way, we'll be joined by an enthusiastic, buck-toothed Banana. Think of him as our friendly companion, a hyped-up commentator, and proverbial class clown. A wildly imaginative creature, the Banana doesn't just react to the stories he's being told—he actively participates in them! In our last adventure, he portrayed Fitcher, a skeezy, bloodthirsty wizard. This time, he'll play a sweet child named Marlene. He's quite the thespian, that Banana. I hope you enjoy his show.

CONTENTS

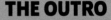

the
INTRO

about the
BROTHERS GRIMM

Once upon a time (the 1800s), in a magical land not far away (a country we now call Germany), there lived two brothers named Jacob and Wilhelm Grimm. The Grimms were on an academic and patriotic mission: to celebrate their German culture through storytelling!

1. JACOB GRIMM   2. WILHELM GRIMM   3. THE BANANA (NOT A GRIMM)

ONCE UPON A TIME, THERE WAS A BANANA...

To accomplish this scholarly feat, the Grimms interviewed local storytellers and transcribed hundreds of old, oral folk tales in danger of being forgotten. They published—and by doing so, preserved—these traditional German stories in a book called *Kinder- und Haüsmarchen* (abbreviated KHM; translated as *Children's Stories and Household Tales*). Even if you've never heard of the Grimm Brothers, there's a 99.82% chance you're familiar with their work. Published in seven editions between 1812 and 1857, KHM has helped preserve well-known fairy tales like *Cinderella, Little Red Riding Hood, Hansel and Gretel, Rumplestiltskin, Snow White*, and more!

THAT IS NOT THE STORY

FUN FACT

The first edition of *Children's Stories and Household Tales* (released in two parts in 1812 and 1815) was not created for children—or households, for that matter! Initially, the Grimms designed KHM more like a cultural research project than a best-selling book. Although the tales were authentic, they weren't much fun to read. The transcriptions felt raw and choppy and the Grimms' overall vibe was academic and dry. Alas, the general public was *not* impressed.

CRITICS ARE *RAVING* ABOUT KHM!

"PATHETIC!"
"TASTELESS JUNK!"

N oting the harsh critiques (and suddenly recognizing KHM's crazy money-making potential), the Grimms began to rework their academic collection for a more lucrative market—kids! Eager to please average families and children, Wilhelm elevated the language, removed the sexual innuendoes, and intensified the violence, *big time!* Clearly, this tactic worked— readers loved KHM's freshly polished, blood-soaked tales! Thus, the Grimms continued to edit, rewrite, and expand their collection for the next forty years. Today, KHM is one of the most influential books of western culture, thanks to the Grimms' persistence and Wilhelm's happy, blood-red pen.

another
FUN FACT

A mong the "tasteless junk," one first-edition tale was so spectacular, so beloved, and so freaking elegant that it was left virtually unchanged since its 1812 publication. In fact, this story was so successful that Wilhelm used it as a quality benchmark to improve subsequent editions of KHM! This magical story is none other than...

THE JUNIPER TREE

1

(YOU PROBABLY SAW THIS COMING)

So what made *The Juniper Tree* such a special snowflake? For starters, it was not an old, oral folk tale (although it was designed to feel like one). *The Juniper Tree* was written by German artist Phillip Otto Runge: a well-known Romantic painter, color theorist, devout Christian, and all-around artsy guy. Given Runge's background, it's not surprising that his fairy tales possess an exceptionally high-brow, artistic flair! Indeed, *The Juniper Tree* is famous for its surreal atmosphere, poignant symbolism, and elegant, poetic style. It's also about beheading a boy and feeding him to his dad.

egads

3

2

PAINTINGS BY PHILLIP OTTO RUNGE

1. *Color Sphere* (1807) **2.** *Self Portrait* (1803)
3. *The Morning* (1808)

The Morning (1808)
Phillip Otto Runge

Don't let Phil's cherubs fool you. *The Juniper Tree* (aka *The Almond Tree*) is one of the most shocking stories in KHM! However, that's not the only reason to love it: For two hundred years, *The Juniper Tree* has enchanted readers with its intense melodrama and dark, otherworldly scenes. I hope you enjoy everything this special snowflake has to offer. And if "enjoyment" is too much of a stretch—well, just try not to puke.

the
STORY

THE JUNIPER TREE

ALSO WITH

The Man

The Woman

The Boy

The Stepmother

The Townsfolk

In true fairy tale style, this unnamed man and woman are the
most exceptional humans to grace the earth. They're kind,
rich, and deliriously slap-happy. But alas—this is a *Grimm* tale.
Happiness is forbidden!

T

he trouble is—aside from being nameless—these perfect folks have just one thing missing from their otherwise-perfect lives: They desperately want a perfect baby so it may inherit their wealth and awesomeness.

YO

PERFECT BABY™
Enlarged to show detail

BABIES 101

SPEAKING OF BABIES, forget those silly creation myths about cabbage patches, storks, and "human biology." In the Grimm universe, babies come from *righteous prayer*. Thus, the good woman gets busy.

She prays...

and prays...

and prays...

BUT FOR SOME REASON, THAT'S NOT WORKING.

One winter's day, the perfect woman is chilling under the
juniper tree that grows in their yard. She's just living her best
life, peeling an apple in the pure, white snow (as you do when
you're a fairy tale character or a social media influencer).

But lo! Suddenly, the blade slips, slicing her formerly perfect finger! I don't know whether frostbite or poor knife skills are to blame, but regardless, the moment is ruined (as is her snack).

INSPIRED

No worries, though. Instead of yowling in pain or
screaming for medical attention, the perfect woman
gets *inspired* by her gushing wound! Apparently, this lady
is the artsy type, for as she stands freezing and bleeding in
the yard, she heaves a deep, poetic sigh and whispers...

THEN SHE FEELS BETTER AND GOES INSIDE.

WARNING

Although wishing is a common pastime in fairy tales, *wishing for children* is a dangerous activity that often leads to absurd misfortune or death. Studies show that kind and beautiful women are in the highest risk group for baby-wishing fatalities. Consider the Grimms' classic victims:

VICTIM #1

SNOW WHITE'S MOTHER

STATUS: Dead

VICTIM #2

RAPUNZEL'S MOTHER

STATUS: Baby placed in witch foster care

VICTIM #3

HANS MY HEDGEHOG'S MOTHER

STATUS: Births a rodent

However, in this fairy tale, the special combo-platter of wishing, bleeding, and Tree Magic™ must've done the trick! Nine months later, the perfect woman gives birth to a perfect baby who is neither an animal nor immediately stolen from her!

And when she sees that her child is as
red as blood and white as snow...

PROMPTLY DROPS DEAD.

VICTIM #4
THE WOMAN
STATUS: Very dead

The man buries her under the juniper tree and cries about being in this spectacularly grim tale.

GNN

GRIMM NEWS NETWORK

Stay Safe

BREAKING NEWS

The Grimms confirm that the woman's cause of death was *happiness.* These are strange, unprecedented times.

Happiness strikes again: *"Her joy was so great that she died!"*

THE FAMILY

VERSION 2.0

On the bright side, it seems the cliché is true: *Time heals wounds, even those inflicted by happiness!* Within a sentence or two, the man stops crying, gets remarried, and has another kid. Fairy tale life is notoriously fast-paced.

THE NEW (BUT NOT NECESSARILY IMPROVED) FAMILY UNIT

1. The red and white boy **2.** The unnamed man from before **3.** The new wife (token evil stepmother) **4.** The non-evil daughter, Marlene*

*Evidently, this story budgeted for only one name

Alas, like most fairy tale widowers, the man must've been on a major rebound after his good wife's death. For whatever reason (depression, loneliness, plot convenience, etc.), his romantic standards have noticibly downgraded. Whereas his first wife was pure and perfect, the second is corrupt and horrible. Also, she's possessed by *Satan*.

But wait—it gets better! Not only is Wife 2.0 a minion of the Antichrist, but she also suffers from a crippling case of *"Murderous Greed!"* Specifically, she's furious that the red and white boy is heir to the family's cash-money. (Archetypal villains aren't great at sharing.) Fortunately, when it comes to being evil, this lady is a real pro. She focuses on her nefarious goals and manages her stress the best way a fairy tale stepmother can: By practicing mindfulness, self-care, and treating the boy like crap.

One day, the stepmother calls to the boy in her sweetest, most non-murderous voice and offers him a bright, shiny apple as a healthy afternoon snack. If the child wants said apple, he may fetch it from the old storage chest. Even in fairy tales, a balanced diet is key.

But lo! As the boy reaches for the nutritious fruit, the stepmother slams the chest shut...

...AND HIS HEAD ROLLS OFF.

THEORIES

This tragic death raises many questions, namely: Why does this fruit bin have a razor-lid? Is this an anti-theft device? A dicey kitchen multitasker? Is *this* what people call "craftsmanship?" Where did the family get this box-of-lawsuits? Here are four theories I just made up.

WHERE THE HECK DID THE FAMILY GET THIS CHEST?

French Revolution souvenir shop

Satan's handmade marketplace

Shady third-party seller

That weird store in the mall that sells pewter wizards, bongos, and ninja stars

Back at the crime
scene, the woman is
pleased with her evil
achievement. Too
bad there's no time
to celebrate, for now
she has a kitchen
to clean and a body
to hide. A mother's
work is never done.

NOTE: Although this is a fairy tale, none of the local woodland critters offer to scrub the walls, clean the pantry, or bleach the blood-stained floor. Hardly seems fair.

Speaking of evidence disposal, how does one hide a body in a Grimm tale? In a world without law enforcement, you'd think this would be a fairly straightforward task: The woman could dig a hole, dump the body, and call it a day. But no! Apparently, the stepmother is craftier than that.

GRIMM CRAFTZ

She reattaches the severed noggin with a chic, white scarf.

She plops a shiny, red apple onto the boy's cold, dead lap...

...and she props him up in the yard like a garden gnome.

Later that day, Marlene finds her favorite monochromatic brother loafing in the yard looking peaceful, stylish—and, if possible—a tinge *whiter* than usual. A shrewd observer, the girl immediately spots the boy's shiny apple and politely asks for a bite. But lo! The pale, motionless boy is unresponsive and does not reply. Understandably, Marlene is devastated. She *needs* that apple.

Like any self-respecting kid, Marlene runs to her mother
to tattle on her rude, apple-hogging brother. Naturally,
the woman instructs the child to follow her dreams and
try reasoning with the boy again. She sends Marlene
back to the garden with this nugget of motherly advice...

Thus emboldened by hunger and idiocy, Marlene attempts to renegotiate with the stone-cold corpse. This time, the valiant girl does not give up. Thanks to her mother, Marlene is now a certified expert in conflict resolution!

SO NOW IT'S *ON*.

...AND HIS HEAD ROLLS OFF.

again.

Marlene scurries home to report the fatal accident and surrender herself to the authorities. She's wild with grief and panic, believing that she has annihilated her only brother, Mortal Kombat® style!

MARLENE WINS

FATALITY

Back at home, the woman comforts her poor, distraught child, who, unfortunately, can't distinguish a living person from a corpse. However, rather than teach Marlene this valuable life skill, the woman decides to frame her for murder instead.

Although poor Marlene is reeling with PTSD, her mother puts her to work in the kitchen anyway. (Fratricide is no excuse for laziness.) Don't worry, though—this is a Grimm tale, so misery has its perks. As Marlene weeps over the cookpot, her tears fall upon the stew, *seasoning it to perfection!* Remember this handy life hack next time you're out of salt—or have just been framed for murder.

GRIMM
IODIZED TEARS

THIS SALT SUPPLIES MISERY, A NECESSARY NUTRIENT

NET WT. 26 OZ (1 LB., 10 OZ.) 737 g

At long last, the man returns! He takes a quick inventory of family members, calculates that a child is missing, and inquires about the red and white boy. Clearly, he hasn't seen tonight's menu.

It's not easy to tell someone that you *braised their child,* so the woman whips up a quick lie. *"The boy has taken a last-minute vacation!"* Ah yes, the sole, legal heir to the family fortune has gone far, far away. And he'll be gone for a long, long time.

The man is bummed that his jet-setting son didn't say goodbye, but in true fairy tale style, gets over it immediately. And who can blame him? It's dinner time and a dude needs to eat. He doesn't feel like discussing trivial matters like the whereabouts of his child.

BESIDES, HE'LL SEE THE BOY AGAIN SOON!

MORAL OF THE STORY

Even the most humble ingredients can be transformed into a delicious, gourmet meal! The man devours the meat like a beast, and in gluttonous ecstasy, hurls the bones to the floor like a deranged Neanderthal. He doesn't question what's in his bowl—whether it's organic, gluten-free, or his firstborn son. He's too busy scarfing it down.

As the man devours the home-grown feast, Marlene slinks away from the table, gathers her brother's bones, and wraps them in her best silk handkerchief. **NOTE:** This is a *tribute*—not a burrito.

Then little Marlene goes to the juniper tree, solemnly lays down the burrito, and cries about being in this spectacularly grim tale.

Suddenly, the clapping tree explodes into a spectacular Vegas-style production, complete with magical mist, smoke, and flame! For the main event, a beautiful red and gold bird bursts from the fire, singing magnificently like a tiny avian Elvis!

But as quickly as it came, the fire extinguishes itself, Elvis-bird flies away, and the juniper tree reverts to its dull, treelike state. Curiously, the bone burrito has vanished! And stranger still is little Marlene's reaction to these dangerous, paranormal events. Prepare for a quote.

"Little Marlene felt just as happy and relieved as if her brother were still alive. She returned home filled with joy and sat down at the table *to eat*."

While the family eats—
whatever they're eating—
the bird heads to town to
run some errands. He soars
above the treetops, singing
the sweetest song...

The Bird
"My Mother (She Slew Me)"
The Juniper Tree
Grimm Records

"My Sister,
Little Marlene,
gathered up my Bones,
tied them up in silk,
and put them under
The Juniper
Tree"

Over in town, My Mother (She Slew Me) is an instant, chart-topping sensation! (The goth scene must be huge here.) Because music streaming hasn't been invented yet, all the local shopkeepers bum-rush the street and beg the creature for an encore. Too bad magic birds never sing twice for free. It's how they get you.

And thus, the business-savvy bird barters his song for a snazzy gold chain, a pair of red shoes, and a giant millstone. **NOTE:** I don't know the going rate for a millstone, but this sounds like a pretty good deal.

Having collected the necessary inventory items to complete
the story, the bird prepares for his grand finale tour. He
slips the millstone around his neck like a bad-ass collar.
Then, with SWAG in claw, he soars back to the juniper tree as
graceful as a bird (a *super-ripped* bird, that is).

Moments later, the family hears—what else—but mellifluous, prophetic squawking coming from the juniper tree! This time, *My Mother, She Slew Me (Reprise)* gets mixed reviews: The man loves it, the woman hates it, and little Marlene is crying again. It's a tough crowd.

Just like the town groupies, the man can't get enough of the bird's catchy tune. Ignoring his wife's protests, he flies outside to catch the live show. As he rushes the juniper tree stage...

Adorned with his new bling, the man scampers inside to tell his family about the incredible gift-dispensing bird. If the creature is passing out free jewelry, perhaps he brought accessories for everyone! Unfortunately, the stepmother is being a real killjoy. Being the only perceptive character in this story, she has balled herself into a fetal position and flat-out refuses to go outside. It's the most sensible reaction we've seen yet. Also, it's nice to know that at least *one* person can hear those lyrics.

Of course, Marlene likes gifts and has no fear of mysterious, human-voiced birds. Therefore, while the man rocks out and the woman cowers in terror, the girl goes outside to claim her prize.

As Marlene approaches the tree, the bird tosses her the red shoes! Impressive. Shoes are a tricky gift.

Meanwhile, the woman has a serious problem (i.e., she knows
the bird has come to destroy her). However, she *also* knows this
feathered minstrel of death is giving away *FREE STUFF!* What's
an evil stepmother to do? After much consideration, her choice
is clear: She gathers her courage, silences her intuition, and
goes outside to get what's coming to her. Maybe it's a pony!

As the woman approaches the juniper tree, the bird lobs down the millstone...

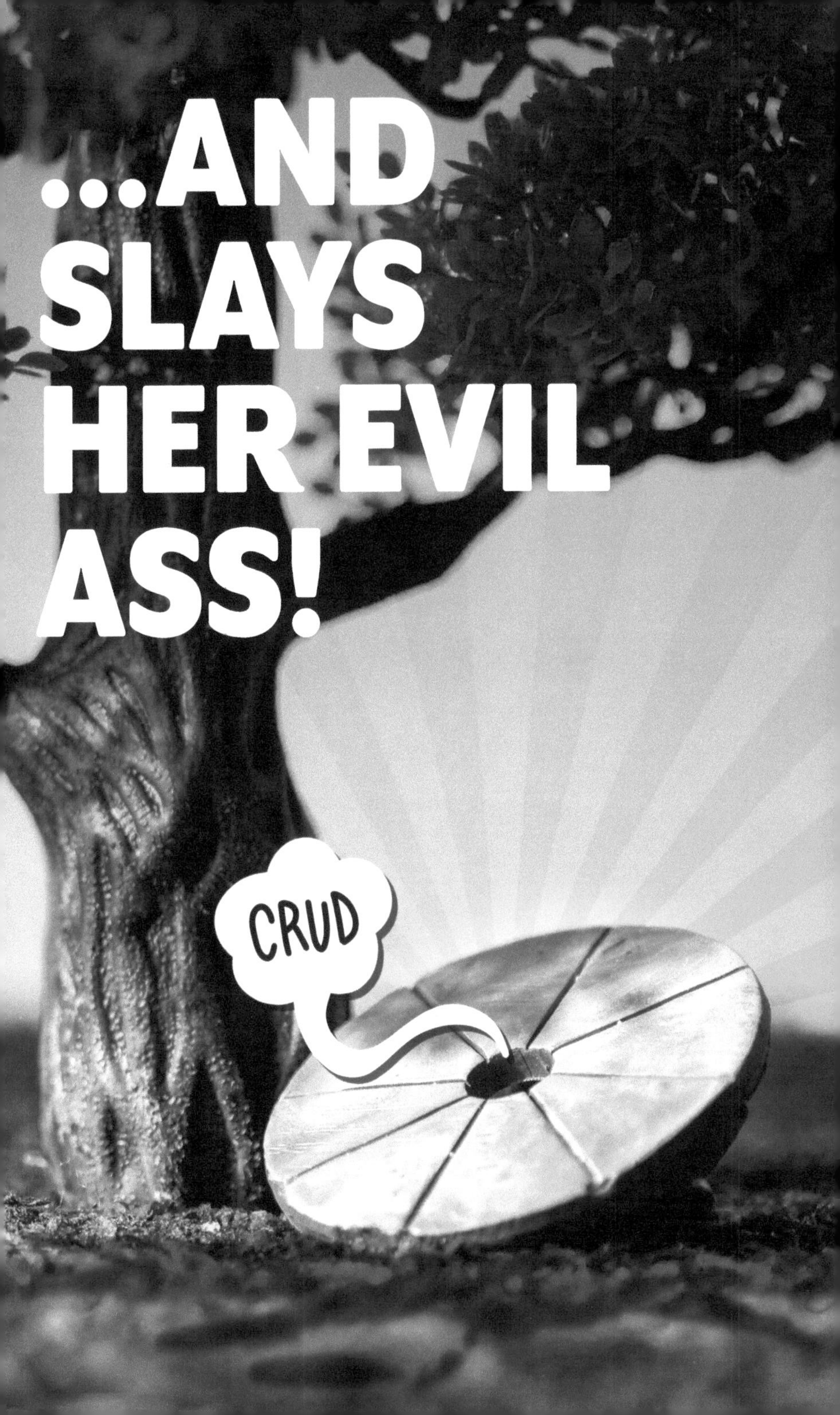
...AND SLAYS HER EVIL ASS!
CRUD

Turbocharged by the gratuitous bloodshed, the juniper tree busts out its signature magic trick one last time. The mist swirls around the millstone (and presumably, the woman's squashed carcass), and *behold!* The red and white boy rematerializes with his cranium securely attached!

And now our spectacular Grimm tale comes to an end.
In true fairy tale style, little Marlene, the unnamed man,
and the resurrected red and white boy celebrate their
reunion as a slap-happy family of three.

Nobody mentions the shape-shifting child, the magic mist, the yard pyrotechnics, or the fact that their dear wife/mother was just massacred by a songbird. All in front of their eyes. Just two seconds ago.

Instead, the man and his children embrace one another,
skip back to the house, and of course...

they
EAT.

The End

the
SCHOLARLY
PART

SIMILAR TALES
from around the world

For ages untold, storytellers have spun delightful tales of murder, cannibalism, and vengeful birds! Even though The Juniper Tree is a literary work, researchers believe that Runge's story was likely inspired by older, oral tales because—*well, that's how this stuff works.* People must like the idea of eating kids because there are hundreds of Juniper Tree-esque fairy tales from around the world. Here's a sample-platter of my four favorites.

the
ROSE TREE
England

Even in fairy tales, at-home haircuts are never a good idea. For example, in *The Rose Tree*, a jealous woman offers to style her stepdaughter's golden hair—but beheads her instead! At least it wasn't a bowl cut.

THE SINGING
BONES
Louisiana

According to this tale's narrator, "When you have twenty-five children, you cannot think of them all the time, and you do not notice if one or two are missing." Excuse me while I call social services.

the
GREEN BIRD
Pakistan

WARNING: Do not cross this green feathered sociopath!
He has a cold heart, a vengeful soul, and a sackful of
needles and nails—which, by the way—he forces his
parents to swallow until they die.

PIPPETY PEW
Scotland

Unlike the woefully clueless man in *The Juniper Tree*, the father in this Scottish tale straight-up knows that his son is in the stew. I would be impressed by his fatherly intuition (or his unsettlingly sharp palate), but he *keeps eating it*.

LYRICS

THE ROSE TREE

"My wicked mother slew me
My dear father ate me
My little brother whom I love
Sits below and I sing above
stick, stock, stone dead!"

THE SINGING BONES

"Our mother killed us,
Our father ate us,
We are not in a coffin,
We are not in the cemetery."

THE GREEN BIRD

"I am the green bird
Who graces this gathering!
My stepmother slaughtered me
And my father devoured me
Only my kind sister
(Allah shower mercy on her!)
Gathered up my bones
And saved them in the urn of stone."

PIPPETY PEW

"Pippety pew!
My mammy me slew
My daddy me ate,
My sister Kate
Gathered all my banes,
And laid them between
Two milk-white stanes.
So a bird I grew,
And away I flew,
Sing Pippety Pew!"

The Folk Tale
STYLE

Researcher Max Lüthi notes that a folk tale's signature style is bold and absurdly minimalistic. (*The Juniper Tree* is so "minimal" that only one character has a name!) Although these stories are notoriously stingy with descriptions, they love to showcase color. According to Lüthi, the folk tale color palette includes natural materials (metal, stone, wood, etc.) and "ultra-pure colors," like gold, silver, black, white, and red. I guess an "orange and beige" boy wouldn't have the same ring to it.

fun with
SYMBOLISM

You may not have noticed with all the severed heads and killer birds flying about, but *The Juniper Tree* is a lovely little tale. Remember the tempting apples? The human stew? The random millstone? As it turns out, one of the most shocking fairy tales of all time is a giant bible reference in disguise. Symbolism is sneaky like that.

JUNIPER

There's more to these trees than just berries and gin. In the bible, junipers are spiritual landmarks where heaven and earth come together. In the Grimm story, the juniper tree represents the tree of life; it's literally where the magic happens! All important events happen at the titular tree, including births, deaths, rebirths, and killer rock concerts.

APPLES

Despite their nutritional value, apples often represent temptation and terribleness. After all, this is the bible's "forbidden fruit" that ruined everything for humankind! It's no coincidence that the Latin word for apple (malus, malum) also means bad, evil, or sin (malum). Anyone familiar with *Snow White* knows that fairy tale apples are irresistible but deadly. Did you notice that each time an apple appears in *The Juniper Tree*, something awful happens? There's no shortage of "malum" in this tale.

THE STEW

Surprise! The most controversial meal in fairy tale history is—a *wafer!* Researchers note that because the red and white boy is a Christ figure, the stew (body and blood of the boy) represents the sacramental Eucharist (body and blood of Christ). Cannibalism's PR department has never looked better.

THE BIRD

A symbol of eternal life, the phoenix is known for its red and gold feathers and its affinity for setting itself on fire. Every 100 years, this mythical freakshow torches its nest and emerges reborn from the ashes. In *The Juniper Tree*, the bird is a Christian symbol, representing the divinely resurrected boy (i.e., Jesus). He's also the story's resident DJ, though he plays only one song (which is stuck on an eternal loop).

MILLSTONE

Sure, revenge is sweet, but—Were there no rocks around? Pointy objects? Fruit chests? Why lug a millstone clear across town? According to scholars, this tedious execution is *poetic justice:* The biblical punishment for child abuse is death-by-millstone! It still seems like a lot of work, though...

"Whoever causes one of these little ones to sin, it would be better for him to have a great millstone fashened around his neck and to be drowned in the depth of the sea."
(Matthew 18:5)

the juniper tree

BEHIND THE TALE

Here's a shocker: Stories that depict wanton violence, human stew, and lawn cadavers tend to be controversial. Although *The Juniper Tree* has ruffled its fair share of feathers, it's also one of the most beloved stories in the Grimms' collection. It seems that whether you love or loathe this tale, you're in great company. On that note, let's explore the dramatic history of *The Juniper Tree* and see what *you* think.

IT WAS PRAISED

1812: Ah, the good old days, when *The Juniper Tree* was one out of only two stories in KHM that critics actually *liked*. (The other was *The Fisherman and His Wife*, another Runge tale.) Readers must've had stronger stomachs back then because about 130-years later...

IT WAS BANNED

1945: In the aftermath of WWII, Allied forces accused the Grimms' tales of promoting violence and corrupting German youth. (It didn't help that Hitler, aka the worst endorser in history, had hijacked KHM for Nazi propaganda.) As one of the Grimms' gnarliest stories, *The Juniper Tree* was singled out for its awfulness and banned in German schools. However, despite its controversial— and at times, legitimately problematic—content, KHM's cultural importance was undeniable. Bans never stuck.

IT WAS CENSORED

1950's: What do you do when you can't ban something? That's right—you censor the ever-living crap out of it! Thus, KHM was *heavily edited* to please modern readers and reflect updated social values. Problematic to the core, *The Juniper Tree* was flat-out removed from most publications. When the tale appeared, it was altered beyond recognition. Of course, all human-sourced meats were taken off the menu.

IT WAS PRAISED...AGAIN

1950's: Amidst the censorship frenzy, fantasy writer J.R.R. Tolkien praised *The Juniper Tree's* "beauty and horror" and argued against changing it. He noted that without the over-the-top gory elements like the extreme violence, bones, and stew, *The Juniper Tree's* powerful, transportive fantasy is lost. In a famous lecture, Tolkien argued that if children must be spared the bones, they should be spared the whole story "until their digestions are stronger." So there we have it from "Mr. Second Breakfast" himself. *The Juniper Tree* is best served with a side of tots. There is no vegan substitute!

IT WAS BJORK'D

1970's and beyond: Tolkien wasn't the only artist inspired by *The Juniper Tree's* dark fantasy. Modern adaptations include:

- **An illustrated book** by Lore Segal and Maurice Sendak (1973)
- **An opera** by Phillip Glass and Robert Moran (1985)
- **A film** starring Icelandic pop star, Bjork (2002)

the JUNIPER TREE

THE BANANA-FREE VERSION

FROM THE GRIMMS'
KINDER UND- HAÜSMARCHEN

Translated by Edgar Taylor
& Marion Edwards

ong, long ago, some two thousand years or so, there lived a rich man with a good and beautiful wife. They loved each other dearly, but sorrowed much that they had no children. So greatly did they desire to have one, that the wife prayed for it day and night, but still they remained childless.

In front of the house there was a court, in which grew a juniper-tree. One winter's day the wife stood under the tree to peel some apples, and as she was peeling them, she cut her finger, and the blood fell on the snow.

'Ah,' sighed the woman heavily, 'if I had but a child, as red as blood and as white as snow,' and as she spoke the words, her heart grew light within her, and it seemed to her that her wish was granted, and she returned to the house feeling glad and comforted.

A month passed, and the snow had all disappeared; then another month went by, and all the earth was green. So the months followed one another, and first the trees budded in the woods, and soon the green branches grew thickly intertwined, and then the blossoms began to fall. Once again the wife stood under the juniper-tree, and it was so full of sweet scent that her heart leaped for joy, and she was so overcome with her happiness, that she fell on her knees. Presently the fruit became round and firm, and she was glad and at peace; but when they were fully ripe she picked the berries and ate eagerly of them, and then she grew sad and ill. A little while later she called her husband, and said to him, weeping. 'If I die, bury me under the juniper-tree.' Then she felt comforted and happy again, and before another month had passed she had a little child, and when she saw that it was as white as snow and as red as blood, her joy was so great that she died.

Her husband buried her under the juniper-tree, and wept bitterly for her. By degrees, however, his sorrow grew less, and although at times he still grieved over his loss, he was able to go about as usual, and later on he married again.

He now had a little daughter born to him; the child of his first wife was a boy, who was as red as blood and as white as snow. The mother loved her daughter very much, and when she looked at her and then looked at the boy, it pierced her heart to think that he would always stand in the way of her own child, and she was continually thinking how she could get the whole of the property for her. This evil thought took possession of her more and more, and made her behave very unkindly to the boy. She drove him from place to place with cuffings and buffetings, so that the poor child went about in fear, and had no peace from the time he left school to the time he went back.

One day the little daughter came running to her mother in the store-room, and said, 'Mother, give me an apple.' '

Yes, my child,' said the wife, and she gave her a beautiful apple out of the chest; the chest had a very heavy lid and a large iron lock.

'Mother,' said the little daughter again, 'may not brother have one too?' The mother was angry at this, but she answered, 'Yes, when he comes out of school.' Just then she looked out of the window and saw him coming, and it seemed as if an evil spirit entered into her, for she snatched the apple out of her little daughter's hand, and said, 'You shall not have one before your brother.' She threw the apple into the chest and shut it to.

The little boy now came in, and the evil spirit in the wife made her say kindly to him, 'My son, will you have an apple?' but she gave him a wicked look.

'Mother,' said the boy, 'how dreadful you look! Yes, give me an apple.' The thought came to her that she would kill him.

'Come with me,' she said, and she lifted up the lid of the chest; 'take one out for yourself.' And as he bent over to do so, the evil spirit urged her, and crash! down went the lid, and off went the little boy's head.

Then she was overwhelmed with fear at the thought of what she had done. 'If only I can prevent anyone knowing that I did it,' she thought. So she went upstairs to her room, and took a white handkerchief out of her top drawer; then she set the boy's head again on his shoulders, and bound it with the handkerchief so that nothing could be seen, and placed him on a chair by the door with an apple in his hand.

Soon after this, little Marleen came up to her mother who was stirring a pot of boiling water over the fire, and said, 'Mother, brother is sitting by the door with an apple in his hand, and he looks so pale; and when I asked him to give me the apple, he did not answer, and that frightened me.'

'Go to him again,' said her mother, 'and if he does not answer, give him a box on the ear.' So little Marleen went, and said, 'Brother, give me that apple,' but he did not say a word; then she gave him a box on the ear, and his head rolled off.

She was so terrified at this, that she ran crying and screaming to her mother. 'Oh!' she said, 'I have knocked off brother's head,' and then she wept and wept, and nothing would stop her.

'What have you done!' said her mother, 'but no one must know about it, so you must keep silence; what is done can't be undone; we will make him into puddings.' And she took the little boy and cut him up, made him into puddings, and put him in the pot. But Marleen stood looking on, and wept and wept, and her tears fell into the pot, so that there was no need of salt.

Presently the father came home and sat down to his dinner; he asked, 'Where is my son?' The mother said nothing, but gave him a large dish of black pudding, and Marleen still wept without ceasing.

The father again asked, 'Where is my son?'

'Oh,' answered the wife, 'he is gone into the country to his mother's great uncle; he is going to stay there some time.'

'What has he gone there for, and he never even said goodbye to me!'

'Well, he likes being there, and he told me he should be away quite six weeks; he is well looked after there.'

'I feel very unhappy about it,' said the husband, 'in case it should not be all right, and he ought to have said goodbye to me.'

With this he went on with his dinner, and said, 'Little Marleen, why do you weep? Brother will soon be back.' Then he asked his wife for more pudding, and as he ate, he threw the bones under the table.

Little Marleen went upstairs and took her best silk handkerchief out of her bottom drawer, and in it she wrapped all the bones from under the table and carried them outside, and all the time she did nothing but weep. Then she laid them in the green grass under the juniper- tree, and she had no sooner done so, then all her sadness seemed to leave her, and she wept no more.

And now the juniper-tree began to move, and the branches waved backwards and forwards, first away from one another, and then together again, as it might be someone clapping their hands for joy.

After this a mist came round the tree, and in the midst of it there was a burning as of fire, and out of the fire there flew a beautiful bird, that rose high into the air, singing magnificently, and when it could no more be seen, the juniper-tree stood there as before, and the silk handkerchief and the bones were gone.

Little Marleen now felt as lighthearted and happy as if her brother were still alive, and she went back to the house and sat down cheerfully to the table and ate.

The bird flew away and alighted on the house of a goldsmith and began to sing:

'My mother killed her little son;
My father grieved when I was gone;
My sister loved me best of all;
She laid her kerchief over me,
And took my bones that they might lie
Underneath the juniper-tree
Kywitt, Kywitt, what a beautiful bird am I!'

The goldsmith was in his workshop making a gold chain, when he heard the song of the bird on his roof. He thought it so beautiful that he got up and ran out, and as he crossed the threshold he lost one of his slippers. But he ran on into the middle of the street, with a slipper on one foot and a sock on the other; he still had on his apron, and still held the gold chain and the pincers in his hands, and so he stood gazing up at the bird, while the sun came shining brightly down on the street.

'Bird,' he said, 'how beautifully you sing! Sing me that song again.'

'Nay,' said the bird, 'I do not sing twice for nothing. Give that gold chain, and I will sing it you again.'

'Here is the chain, take it,' said the goldsmith. 'Only sing me that again.'

The bird flew down and took the gold chain in his right claw, and then he alighted again in front of the goldsmith and sang:

'My mother killed her little son;
My father grieved when I was gone;
My sister loved me best of all;
She laid her kerchief over me,
And took my bones that they might lie
Underneath the juniper-tree
Kywitt, Kywitt, what a beautiful bird am I!'

Then he flew away, and settled on the roof of a shoemaker's house and sang:

'My mother killed her little son;
My father grieved when I was gone;
My sister loved me best of all;
She laid her kerchief over me,
And took my bones that they might lie

Underneath the juniper-tree
Kywitt, Kywitt, what a beautiful bird am I!'

The shoemaker heard him, and he jumped up and ran out in his shirt-sleeves, and stood looking up at the bird on the roof with his hand over his eyes to keep himself from being blinded by the sun.

'Bird,' he said, 'how beautifully you sing!' Then he called through the door to his wife: 'Wife, come out; here is a bird, come and look at it and hear how beautifully it sings.' Then he called his daughter and the children, then the apprentices, girls and boys, and they all ran up the street to look at the bird, and saw how splendid it was with its red and green feathers, and its neck like burnished gold, and eyes like two bright stars in its head.

'Bird,' said the shoemaker, 'sing me that song again.'

'Nay,' answered the bird, 'I do not sing twice for nothing; you must give me something.'

'Wife,' said the man, 'go into the garret; on the upper shelf you will see a pair of red shoes; bring them to me.' The wife went in and fetched the shoes.

'There, bird,' said the shoemaker, 'now sing me that song again.'
The bird flew down and took the red shoes in his left claw, and then he went back to the roof and sang:

'My mother killed her little son;
My father grieved when I was gone;
My sister loved me best of all;
She laid her kerchief over me,
And took my bones that they might lie
Underneath the juniper-tree
Kywitt, Kywitt, what a beautiful bird am I!'

When he had finished, he flew away. He had the chain in his right claw and the shoes in his left, and he flew right away to a mill, and the mill went 'Click clack, click clack, click clack.'

Inside the mill were twenty of the miller's men hewing a stone, and as they went 'Hick hack, hick hack, hick hack,' the mill went 'Click clack, click clack, click clack.' The bird settled on a lime-tree in front of the mill and sang:

'My mother killed her little son;
Then one of the men left off,

My father grieved when I was gone;
Two more men left off and listened,
My sister loved me best of all;
Then four more left off,
She laid her kerchief over me,
And took my bones that they might lie
Now there were only eight at work,
Underneath
And now only five,
the juniper-tree.
And now only one,
Kywitt, Kywitt, what a beautiful bird am I!'
Then he looked up and the last one had left off work.

'Bird,' he said, 'what a beautiful song that is you sing! Let me hear it too; sing it again.'

'Nay,' answered the bird, 'I do not sing twice for nothing; give me that millstone, and I will sing it again.'
'If it belonged to me alone,' said the man, 'you should have it.'

'Yes, yes,' said the others: 'if he will sing again, he can have it.'

The bird came down, and all the twenty millers set to and lifted up the stone with a beam; then the bird put his head through the hole and took the stone round his neck like a collar, and flew back with it to the tree and sang–

'My mother killed her little son;
My father grieved when I was gone;
My sister loved me best of all;
She laid her kerchief over me,
And took my bones that they might lie
Underneath the juniper-tree
Kywitt, Kywitt, what a beautiful bird am I!'

And when he had finished his song, he spread his wings, and with the chain in his right claw, the shoes in his left, and the millstone round his neck, he flew right away to his father's house.
The father, the mother, and little Marleen were having their dinner.

'How lighthearted I feel,' said the father, 'so pleased and cheerful.' 'And I,' said the mother, 'I feel so uneasy, as if a heavy thunderstorm were coming.'

But little Marleen sat and wept and wept. Then the bird came flying towards the house and settled on the roof.

'I do feel so happy,' said the father, 'and how beautifully the sun shines; I feel just as if I were going to see an old friend again.'

'Ah!' said the wife, 'and I am so full of distress and uneasiness that my teeth chatter, and I feel as if there were a fire in my veins,' and she tore open her dress; and all the while little Marleen sat in the corner and wept, and the plate on her knees was wet with her tears.

The bird now flew to the juniper-tree and began singing:

'My mother killed her little son;

The mother shut her eyes and her ears, that she might see and hear nothing, but there was a roaring sound in her ears like that of a violent storm, and in her eyes a burning and flashing like lightning:

My father grieved when I was gone;

'Look, mother,' said the man, 'at the beautiful bird that is singing so magnificently; and how warm and bright the sun is, and what a delicious scent of spice in the air!'

My sister loved me best of all;

Then little Marleen laid her head down on her knees and sobbed.

'I must go outside and see the bird nearer,' said the man.
'Ah, do not go!' cried the wife. 'I feel as if the whole house were in flames!' But the man went out and looked at the bird.

She laid her kerchief over me,
And took my bones that they might lie
Underneath the juniper-tree
Kywitt, Kywitt, what a beautiful bird am I!'

With that the bird let fall the gold chain, and it fell just round the man's neck, so that it fitted him exactly.

He went inside, and said, 'See, what a splendid bird that is; he has given me this beautiful gold chain, and looks so beautiful himself.'

But the wife was in such fear and trouble, that she fell on the floor, and her cap fell from her head.

Then the bird began again:

'My mother killed her little son;

'Ah me!' cried the wife, 'if I were but a thousand feet beneath the earth, that I might not hear that song.'

My father grieved when I was gone;

Then the woman fell down again as if dead.

My sister loved me best of all;

'Well,' said little Marleen, 'I will go out too and see if the bird will give me anything.' So she went out.

She laid her kerchief over me,
And took my bones that they might lie
Underneath the juniper-tree
Kywitt, Kywitt, what a beautiful bird am I!'

And she now felt quite happy and lighthearted; she put on the shoes and danced and jumped about in them. 'I was so miserable,' she said, 'when I came out, but that has all passed away; that is indeed a splendid bird, and he has given me a pair of red shoes.'

The wife sprang up, with her hair standing out from her head like flames of fire. 'Then I will go out too,' she said, 'and see if it will lighten my misery, for I feel as if the world were coming to an end.'

But as she crossed the threshold, crash! the bird threw the millstone down on her head, and she was crushed to death.

The father and little Marleen heard the sound and ran out, but they only saw mist and flame and fire rising from the spot, and when these had passed, there stood the little brother, and he took the father and little Marleen by the hand; then they all three rejoiced, and went inside together and sat down to their dinners and ate.

the
OUTRO

BIBLIOGRAPHY

Biedermann, Hans. *Dictionary of Symbolism: Cultural Icons and the Meanings Behind Them.* Trans. James Hulbert. New York, NY: Facts On File, 1992.

Cashdan, Sheldon. *The Witch Must Die: The Hidden Meaning of Fairy Tales.* New York, NY: Basic Books, 1999.

Haase, Donald. *The Reception of Grimms' Fairy Tales: Responses, Reactions, Revisions.* Detroit, MI: Wayne State University Press, 1993.

Lüthi, Max. *The European Folktale: Form and Nature.* Trans. John D. Niles. Philadelphia: Institute for the Study of Human Issues, 1982

O'Connell, Mark and Airey, Raje. *The Complete Encyclopedia of Signs & Symbols: Identification and analysis of the visual vocabulary that formulates our thoughts and dictates our reactions to the world around us.* London: Hermes House, 2008.

Tatar, Maria. *The Classic Fairy Tales.* New York, NY: Norton, 2017.

Tatar, Maria. *The Annotated Brothers Grimm.* New York, NY: Norton, 2004

Tatar, Maria. "Telling Differences: Parents vs. Children in The Juniper Tree." *Off with their Heads: Fairy Tales and the Culture of Childhood.* Princeton, NJ: Princeton University Press, 1992.

"The Juniper Tree." *BYU Fairy Tales.* Brigham Young University. 25 Aug, 2020 〈http://byufairytales.wordpress.com/thejunipertree/〉

Tolkien, J.R.R., "On Fairy-Stories." *The Monsters and the Critics: And Other Essays.* Boston, MA: Houghton Mifflin, 1984

IMAGES

Cruttwell, Clement., Atlas to Cruttwell's Gazetteer, 1799. Wikimedia Commons, the free media repository.

Crane, Walter. Household Stories from the Collection of the Brothers Grimm. 1882. Wikimedia Commons, the free media repository.

De Juanes, Juan. The Last Supper. 1562. Museo de Prado. Wikimedia Commons, the free media repository.

"File:Grimm1.jpg." Wikimedia Commons, the free media repository.

"File:Phoenix-Fabelwesen.jpg." Wikimedia Commons, the free media repository.

Goble, Warwick. The Juniper Tree. 1899.

Lucas Cranach the Elder. Adam and Eve. 1526. Courtald Institute of Art.Wikimedia Commons, the free media repository.

Medhurst, Phillip. Apocalypse 28. The destruction of Babylon. Revelation cap 18. Mortier's Bible. Phillip Medhurst Collection. Wikimedia Commons, the free media repository. This file is licensed under the Creative Commons Attribution-Share Alike 3.0 Unported license. Image revistion: Cropped from original.

Runge, Phillip Otto. The Morning. 1808. Hamburger Kunsthall. Wikimedia Commons, the free media repository.

Runge, Phillip Otto. Farbenkugel. 1810. Wikimedia Commons, the free media repository.

BANANAGRAPHY

THE SCHOLARLY BANANA

Hello! I'm Karly West, an avid folklore nerd, multi-media artist, and creator of this series! After fifteen years of collecting fairy tales, I was tired of bouncing between beautiful children's books and dense, collegiate texts. There's a huge gap there, and as an adult reading for pleasure, I fall straight into it! Although I enjoy the academic works, I was always looking for a more lighthearted, illustrated book about fairy tales that showcased fun facts that the average reader would enjoy. In 2016, I gave up searching after realizing that I might be the perfect person to create this colorful, bizarre mash-up. So here we are. The Scholarly Banana offers teens and adults a research-focused book about fairy tale history (Scholarly) that's entertaining, artistic, and doesn't take itself too seriously (Banana).

THE ART

I create my illustrations with polymer clay sculptures, photography, and approximately ten gajillion toothpicks. I love the look of classic stop motion films, so I designed The SB to have a similar handcrafted feel. I use Photoshop for basic retouching (wires, toothpicks, and general muck abound), but I intentionally keep the surface imperfections to emphasize that the world you see is constructed from real physical objects. For the final images, I convert the photos to black and white, then paint the colors digitally, one layer at a time. The entire process is just as fun—and just as fiddly—as it sounds. To learn more, visit thescholarlybanana.com.

MUCHOS THANKS!

A warm, Scholarly **thank you** to my family, friends, and fans of The Scholarly Banana series! A special shout-out to my creative confidants: Benjamin West, Marissa Sertich Velie, and Emily Savage Weaver. Without their input and encouragement, I'd probably still be drafting this book.

ALSO IN THE SERIES

The Scholarly Banana Presents Fitcher's Bird: A Classic Fairy Tale from the Brothers Grimm

CPSIA information can be obtained
at www.ICGtesting.com
Printed in the USA
BVHW061811281021
619988BV00001B/2